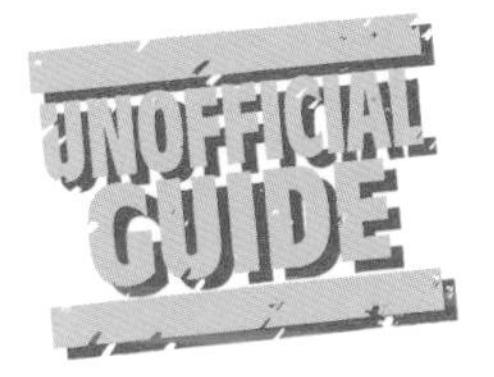
UNOFFICIAL
GUIDE

PARRAGON

First published in 1999 by Parragon

Parragon
Queen Street House
4 Queen Street
Bath BA1 1HE
UK

ISBN 0-75252-916-1

Fixtures are correct at the time of printing but are subject to change in the event of re-arranged matches.

This independent publication has been prepared without any involvement on the part of Liverpool Football Club or the Premier League.

BANK AND PUBLIC HOLIDAYS 1999-2000

England & Wales

Summer Bank Holiday	Monday, August 30
Christmas Day Holiday	Monday, December 27
Boxing Day Holiday	Tuesday, December 28
New Year's Eve Holiday	Friday, December 31
New Year's Day Holiday	Monday, January 3
Good Friday	Friday, April 21
Easter Monday	Monday, April 24
May Day Holiday	Monday, May 1
Spring Bank Holiday	Monday, May 29

Scotland

Summer Bank Holiday	Monday, August 2
Christmas Day Holiday	Monday, December 27
Boxing Day Holiday	Tuesday, December 28
New Year's Eve Holiday	Friday, December 31
New Year's Day Holiday	Monday, January 3
Bank Holiday	Tuesday, January 4
Good Friday	Friday, April 21
Easter Monday	Monday, April 24
Bank Holiday	Monday, May 1
Bank Holiday	Monday, May 29

Northern Ireland

Summer Bank Holiday	Monday, August 30
Christmas Day Holiday	Monday, December 27
Boxing Day Holiday	Tuesday, December 28
New Year's Eve Holiday	Friday, December 31
New Year's Day Holiday	Monday, January 3
St Patrick's Day	Thursday, March 17
Good Friday	Friday, April 21
Easter Monday	Monday, April 24
May Day Holiday	Monday, May 1
Spring Bank Holiday	Monday, May 29
Battle of the Boyne	Wednesday, July 12

Republic of Ireland

Summer Bank Holiday	Monday, August 2
October Holiday	Monday, October 25
Christmas Day Holiday	Monday, December 27
Boxing Day Holiday	Tuesday, December 28
New Year's Eve Holiday	Friday, December 31
New Year's Day Holiday	Monday, January 3
St Patrick's Day	Thursday, March 17
Good Friday	Friday, April 21
Easter Monday	Monday, April 24
May Day Holiday	Monday, May 1
June Holiday	Monday, June 5

CALENDAR 1999

JANUARY

S	M	T	W	T	F	S
					1	2
3	4	5	6	7	8	9
10	11	12	13	14	15	16
17	18	19	20	21	22	23
24/31	25	26	27	28	29	30

FEBRUARY

S	M	T	W	T	F	S
	1	2	3	4	5	6
7	8	9	10	11	12	13
14	15	16	17	18	19	20
21	22	23	24	25	26	27
28						

MARCH

S	M	T	W	T	F	S
	1	2	3	4	5	6
7	8	9	10	11	12	13
14	15	16	17	18	19	20
21	22	23	24	25	26	27
28	29	30	31			

APRIL

S	M	T	W	T	F	S
				1	2	3
4	5	6	7	8	9	10
11	12	13	14	15	16	17
18	19	20	21	22	23	24
25	26	27	28	29	30	

MAY

S	M	T	W	T	F	S
						1
2	3	4	5	6	7	8
9	10	11	12	13	14	15
16	17	18	19	20	21	22
23/30	24/31	25	26	27	28	29

JUNE

S	M	T	W	T	F	S
		1	2	3	4	5
6	7	8	9	10	11	12
13	14	15	16	17	18	19
20	21	22	23	24	25	26
27	28	29	30			

JULY

S	M	T	W	T	F	S
				1	2	3
4	5	6	7	8	9	10
11	12	13	14	15	16	17
18	19	20	21	22	23	24
25	26	27	28	29	30	31

AUGUST

S	M	T	W	T	F	S
1	2	3	4	5	6	7
8	9	10	11	12	13	14
15	16	17	18	19	20	21
22	23	24	25	26	27	28
29	30	31				

SEPTEMBER

S	M	T	W	T	F	S
			1	2	3	4
5	6	7	8	9	10	11
12	13	14	15	16	17	18
19	20	21	22	23	24	25
26	27	28	29	30		

OCTOBER

S	M	T	W	T	F	S
					1	2
3	4	5	6	7	8	9
10	11	12	13	14	15	16
17	18	19	20	21	22	23
24/31	25	26	27	28	29	30

NOVEMBER

S	M	T	W	T	F	S
	1	2	3	4	5	6
7	8	9	10	11	12	13
14	15	16	17	18	19	20
21	22	23	24	25	26	27
28	29	30				

DECEMBER

S	M	T	W	T	F	S
			1	2	3	4
5	6	7	8	9	10	11
12	13	14	15	16	17	18
19	20	21	22	23	24	25
26	27	28	29	30	31	

CALENDAR 2000

JANUARY

S	M	T	W	T	F	S
						1
2	3	4	5	6	7	8
9	10	11	12	13	14	15
16	17	18	19	20	21	22
23/30	24/31	25	26	27	28	29

FEBRUARY

S	M	T	W	T	F	S
		1	2	3	4	5
6	7	8	9	10	11	12
13	14	15	16	17	18	19
20	21	22	23	24	25	26
27	28	29				

MARCH

S	M	T	W	T	F	S
			1	2	3	4
5	6	7	8	9	10	11
12	13	14	15	16	17	18
19	20	21	22	23	24	25
26	27	28	29	30	31	

APRIL

S	M	T	W	T	F	S
						1
2	3	4	5	6	7	8
9	10	11	12	13	14	15
16	17	18	19	20	21	22
23/30	24	25	26	27	28	29

MAY

S	M	T	W	T	F	S
	1	2	3	4	5	6
7	8	9	10	11	12	13
14	15	16	17	18	19	20
21	22	23	24	25	26	27
28	29	30	31			

JUNE

S	M	T	W	T	F	S
				1	2	3
4	5	6	7	8	9	10
11	12	13	14	15	16	17
18	19	20	21	22	23	24
25	26	27	28	29	30	

JULY

S	M	T	W	T	F	S
						1
2	3	4	5	6	7	8
9	10	11	12	13	14	15
16	17	18	19	20	21	22
23/30	24/31	25	26	27	28	29

AUGUST

S	M	T	W	T	F	S
		1	2	3	4	5
6	7	8	9	10	11	12
13	14	15	16	17	18	19
20	21	22	23	24	25	26
27	28	29	30	31		

SEPTEMBER

S	M	T	W	T	F	S
					1	2
3	4	5	6	7	8	9
10	11	12	13	14	15	16
17	18	19	20	21	22	23
24	25	26	27	28	29	30

OCTOBER

S	M	T	W	T	F	S
1	2	3	4	5	6	7
8	9	10	11	12	13	14
15	16	17	18	19	20	21
22	23	24	25	26	27	28
29	30	31				

NOVEMBER

S	M	T	W	T	F	S
			1	2	3	4
5	6	7	8	9	10	11
12	13	14	15	16	17	18
19	20	21	22	23	24	25
26	27	28	29	30		

DECEMBER

S	M	T	W	T	F	S
					1	2
3	4	5	6	7	8	9
10	11	12	13	14	15	16
17	18	19	20	21	22	23
24/31	25	26	27	28	29	30

CALENDAR 2001

JANUARY

S	M	T	W	T	F	S
	1	2	3	4	5	6
7	8	9	10	11	12	13
14	15	16	17	18	19	20
21	22	23	24	25	26	27
28	29	30	31			

FEBRUARY

S	M	T	W	T	F	S
				1	2	3
4	5	6	7	8	9	10
11	12	13	14	15	16	17
18	19	20	21	22	23	24
25	26	27	28			

MARCH

S	M	T	W	T	F	S
				1	2	3
4	5	6	7	8	9	10
11	12	13	14	15	16	17
18	19	20	21	22	23	24
25	26	27	28	29	30	31

APRIL

S	M	T	W	T	F	S
1	2	3	4	5	6	7
8	9	10	11	12	13	14
15	16	17	18	19	20	21
22	23	24	25	26	27	28
29	30					

MAY

S	M	T	W	T	F	S
		1	2	3	4	5
6	7	8	9	10	11	12
13	14	15	16	17	18	19
20	21	22	23	24	25	26
27	28	29	30	31		

JUNE

S	M	T	W	T	F	S
					1	2
3	4	5	6	7	8	9
10	11	12	13	14	15	16
17	18	19	20	21	22	23
24	25	26	27	28	29	30

JULY

S	M	T	W	T	F	S
1	2	3	4	5	6	7
8	9	10	11	12	13	14
15	16	17	18	19	20	21
22	23	24	25	26	27	28
29	30	31				

AUGUST

S	M	T	W	T	F	S
			1	2	3	4
5	6	7	8	9	10	11
12	13	14	15	16	17	18
19	20	21	22	23	24	25
26	27	28	29	30	31	

SEPTEMBER

S	M	T	W	T	F	S
						1
2	3	4	5	6	7	8
9	10	11	12	13	14	15
16	17	18	19	20	21	22
23/30	24	25	26	27	28	29

OCTOBER

S	M	T	W	T	F	S
	1	2	3	4	5	6
7	8	9	10	11	12	13
14	15	16	17	18	19	20
21	22	23	24	25	26	27
28	29	30	31			

NOVEMBER

S	M	T	W	T	F	S
				1	2	3
4	5	6	7	8	9	10
11	12	13	14	15	16	17
18	19	20	21	22	23	24
25	26	27	28	29	30	

DECEMBER

S	M	T	W	T	F	S
						1
2	3	4	5	6	7	8
9	10	11	12	13	14	15
16	17	18	19	20	21	22
23/30	24/31	25	26	27	28	29

LIVERPOOL FC

Anfield Road
Liverpool L4 0TH

Tel:	(0151) 263 2361
Fax:	(0151) 260 8813
Ticket And Match Info:	(0151) 260 9999/8680
Credit Card Bookings	(0151) 260 6677
LFC Direct Mail Order	(0990) 532532
Club Call:	0891 12 11 84

THE PREMIER LEAGUE

16 Lancaster Gate
London W2 3LW

Tel:	(0171) 262 4542

OUR DAYS ARE NUMBERED FANZINE

103 Acanthus Road
Liverpool L13 3DY

Carlsberg

THE LIVERPOOL STORY

When it comes to the world's most famous football clubs, the name of Liverpool FC is known everywhere from Zanzibar to New Zealand. Few would doubt the club retains that status today – but it must also be admitted that they are relying on past glories, the most recent decade having seen just three trophies reaching the Anfield Road trophy room.

Having employed their tried and tested method of promotion from within by elevating former player Roy Evans to the hot seat, the board started 1998-99 with a new injection of continental ideas when they introduced Gérard Houllier, a former French national coach, as joint manager. Sadly, the experiment of power sharing proved unsuccessful, and as Liverpool FC, established 1892, enters the new millennium it is Houllier alone who bears the

LIVERPOOL FACTFILE

Year formed:	1892
Ground:	Anfield Road, Liverpool L4 0TH
Nickname:	The Reds
Club colours:	Red
Manager:	Gérard Houllier
Record attendance:	61,905 v Wolverhampton Wanderers, 2 Feb 1952, FA Cup Fourth Round
Record League victory:	10-1 v Rotherham Town, 18 Feb 1896, Div Two
Record Cup victory:	11-0 v Stromsgodset Drammen, 17 Sept 1974, European Cup Winners' Cup First Round first leg
Record defeat:	1-9 v Birmingham City, 11 Dec 1954, Div Two
Most League goals (season):	Roger Hunt, 41, 1961-62, Div Two
Most League goals (career):	Roger Hunt, 245, 1959-69
Most League appearances:	Ian Callaghan, 640, 1960-78

responsibility of bringing success back to the Red half of Merseyside. His is a team of nations, with players from all corners of the globe reflecting Liverpool's worldwide fame. This is the season he – and they – must deliver the goods.

The story of Liverpool FC begins, strangely, with Everton. Having played at Anfield since 1884, the Blues moved the short distance to Goodison Park, leaving ground owner John Houlding to form a new club that took the city's name as its own. Manager John McKenna stocked his team with Scots, a tactic that paid quick dividends as Liverpool won promotion in their very first Football League season.

Tom Watson was in charge when they won their first Championship in 1901 but, unable to keep up the pace, they were relegated in 1903-04. They not only came straight back up but took their second League Championship in 1905-06. Celebrations would be short-lived, though, and the Reds' only further success before the 1914-18 war came with a first FA Cup Final appearance against Burnley at Crystal Palace, lost by a single goal.

Liverpool won their third League title in the 1921-22 season and retained the Championship the next year, thanks to 21 clean sheets from goalkeeper Elisha Scott; sharpshooter Harry Chambers was top scorer on both occasions. But a fifth Championship would elude Liverpool until after the Second World War was over.

Billy Liddell, Jack Balmer and Albert Stubbins (who scored hat-tricks in three consecutive games) helped Liverpool lift the title again in 1946-47. Bob Paisley, who as manager would later guide the Reds through their most successful period, played the first of his 278 games this season, but was absent for Liverpool's second FA Cup Final defeat, this time 2-0 to Arsenal in 1950. Nearly 50 unbroken top-flight years ended with relegation in 1954, and it took the arrival of the mighty Bill Shankly at Anfield as manager five years later to stop the rot.

Shankly, a former Scotland International, wasted no time rebuilding the team, with the likes of Chris Lawler and Ian Callaghan among its home-grown backbone. Scots Ian St John and Ron Yeats arrived from Motherwell and Dundee United respectively to help the team to the Second Division title, striker Roger Hunt's 41 goals including a club record five hat-tricks.

Championships in 1964 and 1966 sandwiched the club's first ever FA Cup victory, 2-1 over Leeds United. The World Cup year of 1966 (Roger Hunt appearing in the Final) saw Liverpool only just miss out in the Cup Winners' Cup, losing 2-1 to Borussia Dortmund in the Final after extra time. The Reds would eventually win their first European trophy in 1973 against another German side, Borussia Moenchengladbach. The team that won the UEFA Cup 3-2 on aggregate featured a new international élite of Ray Clemence, Emlyn Hughes and Steve Heighway, as well as strikers John Toshack and Kevin Keegan. Shankly bowed out on a high after the 3-0 win against Newcastle in the 1974 FA Cup Final, recommending Bob Paisley as his successor.

Paisley's first season in charge was trophyless, but in 1975-76 came the League and a second UEFA Cup. The Championship was retained the following season – and the European Cup added to it, Liverpool beating Borussia Moenchengladbach 3-1 in Rome on a famous night.

A Germany-bound Keegan was replaced by Kenny Dalglish from Celtic and the newcomer would net the winning goal as Liverpool retained the European Cup, beating FC Brugge 1-0 at Wembley. Nottingham Forest foiled a Euro hat-trick, but the 1978-79 season saw the Reds amass a record 68 points to take the League yet again. It was the same story in 1980.

Dominic Matteo/Patrik Berger ▶

MATTEO
21
BERGER
15

HONOURS BOARD

1893-94	Division Two Champions
1895-96	Division Two Champions
1898-99	Division One Runners-up
1900-01	Division One Champions
1904-05	Division Two Champions
1905-06	Division One Champions
1909-10	Division One Runners-up
1913-14	FA Cup Runners-up
1921-22	Division One Champions
1922-23	Division One Champions
1946-47	Division One Champions
1949-50	FA Cup Runners-up
1961-62	Division Two Champions
1963-64	Division One Champions
1964-65	FA Cup Winners
1965-66	Division One Champions and European Cup Winners' Cup Runners-up
1968-69	Division One Runners-up
1970-71	FA Cup Runners-up
1972-73	Division One Champions and UEFA Cup Winners
1973-74	Division One Runners-up and FA Cup Winners
1974-75	Division One Runners-up
1975-76	Division One Champions and UEFA Cup Winners
1976-77	Division One Champions, FA Cup Runners-up, European Cup Winners and European Super Cup Winners
1977-78	Division One Runners-up, League Cup Runners-up and European Cup Winners
1978-79	Division One Champions
1979-80	Division One Champions
1980-81	League Cup Winners, European Cup Winners and World Club Championship Runners-up
1981-82	Division One Champions and League Cup Winners
1982-83	Division One Champions and League Cup Winners
1983-84	Division One Champions, League Cup Winners and European Cup Winners
1984-85	Division One Runners-up and European Cup Runners-up
1985-86	Division One Champions, FA Cup Winners and League Super Cup Winners
1986-87	Division One Runners-up and League Cup Runners-up
1987-88	Division One Champions and FA Cup Runners-up
1988-89	Division One Runners-up and FA Cup Winners
1989-90	Division One Champions
1990-91	Division One Runners-up
1991-92	FA Cup Winners
1994-95	League Cup Winners
1995-96	FA Cup Runners-up

Villa took the Championship in 1981, but this was the year the Reds won their first of four consecutive League Cups, beating West Ham 2-1 in a replay. The Reds also won their customary European Cup, beating Real Madrid 1-0 in Paris. Bob Paisley was now the most successful manager in history and Liverpool the most successful club. League Championships came in 1982, 1983, 1984, 1986, 1988 and 1990 as well as a fourth European Cup win in 1984 as Welsh wizard Ian Rush became the Kop's new hero. The Heysel tragedy in 1985 ended Liverpool's run in European competition, Bob Paisley having made way for another boot-room boy, Joe Fagan, who guided the Reds to three trophies before retiring.

The much-respected Kenny Dalglish became the Reds' first ever player-manager in 1985. He immediately fashioned a League and FA Cup Double, adding John Barnes and Peter Beardsley to his squad as the 1980s ended. An FA Cup win in 1989 was his last knockout competition honour as he resigned two years later, citing the pressure of the job. But all the team's accomplishments on the pitch were overshadowed by the tragedy at Hillsborough where 96 Liverpool fans died during an FA Cup Semi-Final.

Dalglish's successor, former player Graeme Souness, had achieved much north of the border with Rangers but while back at Anfield failed to create a team capable of challenging for top honours. A 1992 FA Cup win would prove his only trophy, while Roy Evans, an Anfield stalwart on the playing staff since the 1960s, could only claim the League Cup in 1995. Liverpool's expectations were clearly higher than most other clubs' and despite three successive top four placings for his team the likeable Evans was not meeting them.

He had the benefit of home-grown stars like Robbie Fowler and Michael Owen, both of whom became full England internationals, yet signings to augment them like the troubled Stan Collymore and flying winger Mark Kennedy failed to make the anticipated impact. The only consolation was Everton's languishing even further down the table. November 1998 saw the Liverpool board admit the joint managerial structure, tried and rejected by Charlton a few years before, was not working. Houllier assumed total control, Evans leaving the club with regret despite having been offered an alternative role.

It was a drastic step, but the Reds still could not drag themselves up to a European place. Star winger Steve McManaman made clear his wish to leave, and it became clear that Gérard Houllier faced a big challenge to steer the Reds back to the top. This he showed his determination to do with a summer 1999 spending spree that brought many big names to the club from Europe. Dutch goalkeeper Sander Westerveld became the £4 million last line of defence, while giant centre-back Sami Hyypia would play in front of him.

Other newcomers include Tita Camara (France) and Stephane Henchoz (Switzerland), suggesting that though more exotic faces now starred in place of Shankly's Scots the intention was the same – to revitalise a sleeping giant and return Liverpool to the position of authority their supporters demanded. The absence of European fixtures for the first time in five years gave the team the chance to concentrate on domestic excellence – the initial foundation of global success.

Robbie Fowler ▶

9

1999-2000 FIXTURES

FA Carling Premiership

Date	Opponents	Venue	Previous Results 98-99	97-98	96-97
Aug 7	Sheffield Wednesday	(A)	0-1	2-1	1-1
11	West Ham United	(H)	2-2	5-0	0-0
14	Watford	(H)	—	—	—
21	Middlesbrough	(A)	3-1	—	3-3
23	Leeds United	(A)	0-0	2-0	2-0
28	Arsenal	(H)	0-0	4-0	2-0
Sep 11	Manchester United	(H)	2-2	1-3	1-3
18	Leicester City	(A)	0-1	0-0	3-0
27	Everton	(H)	3-2	1-1	1-1
Oct 2	Aston Villa	(A)	4-2	1-2	0-1
16	Chelsea	(H)	1-1	4-2	5-1
23	Southampton	(A)	2-1	1-1	1-0
30	Bradford City	(H)	—	—	—
Nov 6	Derby County	(H)	1-2	4-0	2-1
20	Sunderland	(A)	—	—	2-1
27	West Ham United	(A)	1-2	1-2	2-1
Dec 4	Sheffield Wednesday	(H)	2-0	2-1	0-1
18	Coventry City	(H)	2-0	1-0	1-2
26	Newcastle United	(A)	4-1	2-1	1-1
28	Wimbledon	(H)	3-0	2-0	1-1
Jan 3	Tottenham Hotspur	(A)	1-2	3-3	2-0
15	Watford	(A)	—	—	—
22	Middlesbrough	(H)	3-1	—	5-1
Feb 5	Leeds United	(H)	1-3	3-1	4-0

1999-2000 FIXTURES

FA Carling Premiership

Date	Opponents	Venue	Previous Results 98-99	97-98	96-97
12	Arsenal	(A)	0-0	1-0	2-1
26	Leicester City	(H)	0-1	1-2	1-1
Mar 4	Manchester United	(A)	0-2	1-1	0-1
11	Sunderland	(H)	—	—	0-0
18	Derby County	(A)	2-3	0-1	1-0
25	Newcastle United	(H)	4-2	1-0	4-3
Apr 1	Coventry City	(A)	1-2	1-1	1-0
8	Tottenham Hotspur	(H)	3-2	4-0	2-1
15	Wimbledon	(A)	0-1	1-1	1-2
22	Everton	(A)	0-0	0-2	1-1
24	Aston Villa	(H)	0-1	3-0	3-0
29	Chelsea	(A)	1-2	1-4	0-1
May 6	Southampton	(H)	7-1	2-3	2-1
14	Bradford City	(A)	—	—	—

Axa FA Cup

Dec 11	Third Round
Jan 8	Fourth Round
29	Fifth Round
Feb 19	Sixth Round
Apr 9	Semi-Final
May 20	Final

Worthington Cup

Sep 15	Second Round 1
22	Second Round 2
Oct 13	Third Round
Dec 1	Fourth Round
15	Fifth Round
Jan 12	Semi-Final 1
26	Semi-Final 2
Feb 27	Final

26 Monday

27 Tuesday

28 Wednesday

29 Thursday

30 Friday

31 Saturday

1 Sunday

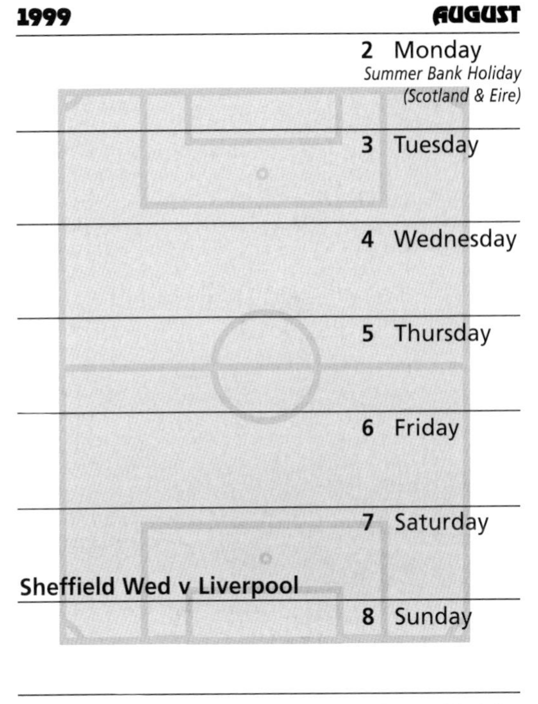

2 Monday
Summer Bank Holiday (Scotland & Eire)

3 Tuesday

4 Wednesday

5 Thursday

6 Friday

7 Saturday

Sheffield Wed v Liverpool

8 Sunday

This Time Last Year...

Kicking off a season with two managers was unique even in the history of a club that's been there, seen that and won the trophy – and Messrs Houllier and Evans started with an unbeaten month. Two away wins plus a draw against the reigning Champions is hard to top. And Michael Owen, continuing his World Cup form with a hat-trick at St James' Park, was indisputably man of the moment. Now a full international, he was expected to link with Robbie Fowler up front – but with Fowler still fighting injury, his first partner was German ace Karlheinz Riedle who scored the campaign's opening goal against Southampton.

Thrills To Come...

The earlier start to this season means the Reds will have played six games – double the 1998 total – by the end of August. And guess what? The last of them is a home clash with Arsenal! For the first time in many years, the Reds won't be playing in Europe, and this may give them the edge against their title-chasing rivals. An away clash with Leeds is the best of the rest.

This Month Last Season

Date	Comp	Venue	Opposition	Result
16	PL	A	Southampton	2-1
22	PL	H	Arsenal	0-0
30	PL	A	Newcastle Utd	4-1

Michael Owen ▶

9 Monday

10 Tuesday

11 Wednesday

Liverpool v West Ham United

12 Thursday

13 Friday

14 Saturday

Liverpool v Watford

15 Sunday

16 Monday

17 Tuesday

Oyvind Leonhardsen born in Kristiansund, Norway (1970).

18 Wednesday

19 Thursday

20 Friday

21 Saturday

Middlesbrough v Liverpool

22 Sunday

23 Monday

Leeds United v Liverpool

24 Tuesday

25 Wednesday

26 Thursday

27 Friday

28 Saturday

Emlyn Hughes born in Barrow-in-Furness (1947).

Liverpool v Arsenal

29 Sunday

30 Monday
Summer Bank Holiday (England, Wales & NI)

31 Tuesday

1 Wednesday

2 Thursday

Bill Shankly born in Glenbuck (1913).

3 Friday

Gérard Houllier born in Lille, France (1947).

4 Saturday

5 Sunday

This Time Last Year...

Eight goals without reply against UEFA Cup opponents Kosice suggested this was going to be a spectacular campaign. At home, though, it was another story, with no points gained on travels to Upton Park and Old Trafford. The visit of Charlton, a home banker if ever there was one, resulted in many long faces after Robbie Fowler, in his first game of the season after injury, seemed to clinch a 3-2 win against the ten-men visitors only for Steve Jones to equalise...but at least Coventry were beaten! David James was restored to the first team in place of American Brad Friedel after the Manchester United defeat, beginning a run that would last through until late April.

Thrills To Come...

This season it's Man United again, at home this time, plus a visit from Merseyside neighbours Everton and a trip to Filbert Street sandwiched in-between.

This Month Last Season

Date	Comp	Venue	Opposition	Result
9	PL	H	Coventry C	2-0
12	PL	A	West Ham Utd	1-2
15	UEFA	A	Kosice	3-0
19	PL	H	Charlton Ath	3-3
24	PL	A	Manchester Utd	0-2
29	UEFA	H	Kosice	5-0

Jamie Redknapp ▶

Carlsberg

6 Monday

7 Tuesday

Stephane Henchoz born in Billens, Switzerland (1974).

8 Wednesday

Haukua Gudnason born in Keflavik, Iceland (1978).

9 Thursday

Jean-Michel Ferri born in France (1969).

10 Friday

11 Saturday

Liverpool v Man United

12 Sunday

David Thompson born in Birkenhead (1977).

13 Monday

14 Tuesday

15 Wednesday

Worthington Cup Second Round 1

16 Thursday

Karlheinz Riedle born in Weiler, Germany (1965).

17 Friday

Record Cup victory: 11-0 v Stromsgodset (1974).

18 Saturday

Leicester C v Liverpool

19 Sunday

20 Monday

21 Tuesday

22 Wednesday

Worthington Cup Second Round 2

23 Thursday

24 Friday

25 Saturday

26 Sunday

27 Monday

Liverpool v Everton

28 Tuesday

First competitive fixture at Anfield as Everton beat Earlstown 5-0 (1884).

29 Wednesday

Legendary manager Bill Shankly dies (1981).

30 Thursday

1 Friday

2 Saturday

Aston Villa v Liverpool

3 Sunday

OCTOBER ACTION

This Time Last Year...

Draws against Vialli's Chelsea (a late Jamie Redknapp rescue act) and neighbours Everton were followed by a five-goal thrashing of Forest, already looking down and out. Michael Owen got four but, like his fellow forwards, couldn't notch against Valencia, leaving the Spaniards favourites to go through to the UEFA Cup Third Round. The Worthington Cup brought Second Division Fulham to Anfield with future England manager Kevin Keegan at the helm – but even the former Kop favourite couldn't bridge the gap in class between the teams.

Thrills To Come...

A first visit from former Liverpool reserve Paul Jewell's Bradford City ends a month that brings trips down the M6 to Villa Park and even further to the Dell, plus a visit from multi-national megaspenders Chelsea, Deschamps and all.

This Month Last Season

Date	Comp	Venue	Opposition	Result
4	PL	H	Chelsea	1-1
17	PL	A	Everton	0-0
20	UEFA	H	Valencia	0-0
24	PL	H	Nott'm Forest	5-1
27	WC	H	Fulham	3-1
31	PL	A	Leicester C	0-1

Robbie Fowler ▶

Carlsberg
SHOWER

4 Monday

5 Tuesday

6 Wednesday

Bruce Grobbelaar born in Durban, South Africa (1957).

7 Thursday

Sami Hyypia born in Poorvo, Finland (1973).

8 Friday

9 Saturday

10 Sunday

11 Monday

12 Tuesday

13 Wednesday

First Merseyside derby sees Everton win 3-0 (1894).

Worthington Cup Third Round

14 Thursday

15 Friday

16 Saturday

Liverpool v Chelsea

17 Sunday

18 Monday

19 Tuesday

20 Wednesday

Ian Rush born in St Asaph (1961).

21 Thursday

Paul Ince born in Ilford (1967).

22 Friday

23 Saturday

Sander Westerveld born in Enschede, Holland (1974).

Southampton v Liverpool

24 Sunday
Summer Time Ends

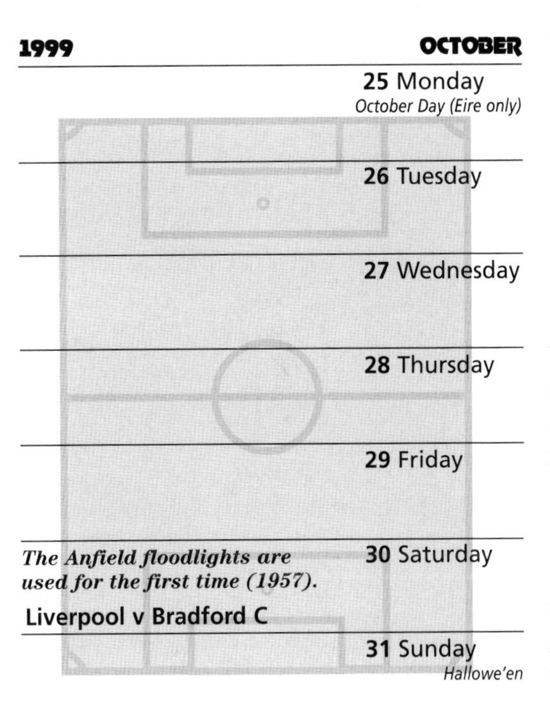

25 Monday
October Day (Eire only)

26 Tuesday

27 Wednesday

28 Thursday

29 Friday

30 Saturday

The Anfield floodlights are used for the first time (1957).

Liverpool v Bradford C

31 Sunday
Hallowe'en

NOVEMBER ACTION

This Time Last Year...

Two home defeats on the bounce, unthinkable in days of old, against Derby and Leeds plus a League Cup reverse to Spurs are enough to confirm Roy Evans' departure after three decades as player and boot-room stalwart. Villa and Blackburn feel the lash to end this month of fireworks after the earlier damp squibs. Not to be outdone by his wonderkid partner, Robbie Fowler notches a Villa Park hat-trick with Paul Ince on the scoresheet for the first time this season. He obviously liked the feeling because he opened the scoring against Blackburn as well!

Thrills To Come...

Sunderland's Stadium of Light beckons for a deadly-serious re-run of the friendly the Reds played at the end of last season. West Ham United (away) and a visit from Derby County complete the Premiership calendar.

This Month Last Season

Date	Comp	Venue	Opposition	Result
3	UEFA	A	Valencia	2-2
7	PL	H	Derby County	1-2
10	WC	H	Tottenham H	1-3
14	PL	H	Leeds Utd	1-3
21	PL	A	Aston Villa	4-2
24	UEFA	A	Celta Vigo	1-3
29	PL	H	Blackburn R	2-0

Gérard Houllier/Roy Evans ▶

NIKE

1 Monday

2 Tuesday

3 Wednesday

4 Thursday

5 Friday
Guy Fawkes Night

6 Saturday

Liverpool v Derby Co

7 Sunday
Remembrance Sunday

John Barnes born in Jamaica (1963).

8 Monday

9 Tuesday

Patrik Berger born in Prague, Czech Republic (1973).

10 Wednesday

11 Thursday

Gérard Houllier becomes manager as Roy Evans leaves Anfield (1998).

12 Friday

13 Saturday

14 Sunday

15 Monday

16 Tuesday

17 Wednesday

Titi Camara born in France (1972).

18 Thursday

19 Friday

20 Saturday

Sunderland v Liverpool

21 Sunday

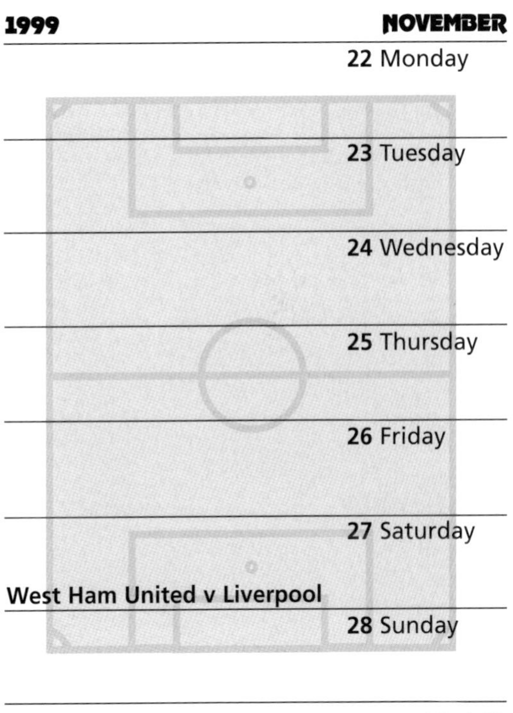

22 Monday

23 Tuesday

24 Wednesday

25 Thursday

26 Friday

27 Saturday

West Ham United v Liverpool

28 Sunday

This Time Last Year...

A month that started with back-to-back defeats against Londoners Spurs and Wimbledon lightened with a pre-Xmas win against Sheffield Wednesday. Christmas festivities were then assured with away wins against Boro and Newcastle. The impressive win at St James' Park, with two goals apiece from Owen and Riedle, was achieved without Paul Ince and Robbie Fowler. In Europe, having eliminated Valencia magnificently on away goals from McManaman and Berger, the Reds failed to repeat the feat against Celta Vigo.

Thrills To Come...

It's Newcastle away again this time round on Boxing Day, washed down by a taste of Wimbledon at home! Anfield clashes with Sheffield and Coventry offer the alternative to Christmas shopping, while the FA Cup Third Round falls in December for the first time. Could this be the year?

This Month Last Season

Date	Comp	Venue	Opposition	Result
5	PL	A	Tottenham H	1-2
8	UEFA	H	Celta Vigo	0-1
13	PL	A	Wimbledon	0-1
19	PL	H	Sheffield Wed	2-0
26	PL	A	Middlesbrough	3-1
28	PL	H	Newcastle Utd	4-2

Jamie Carragher ▶

Carlsberg

29 Monday

30 Tuesday
St Andrew's Day

Phil Babb born in Lambeth (1970).

1 Wednesday

Worthington Cup Fourth Round

2 Thursday

3 Friday

4 Saturday

Liverpool v Sheffield Wed

5 Sunday

6 Monday

Record European defeat as Ajax win 5-0 (1966). Sean Dundee born in South Africa (1972).

7 Tuesday

8 Wednesday

9 Thursday

10 Friday

Stig-Inge Bjornebye born in Elverum, Norway (1969).

FA Cup Third Round

11 Saturday

12 Sunday

13 Monday

14 Tuesday

Michael Owen born in Chester (1979).

15 Wednesday

Worthington Cup Fifth Round

16 Thursday

17 Friday

18 Saturday

Liverpool v Coventry C

19 Sunday

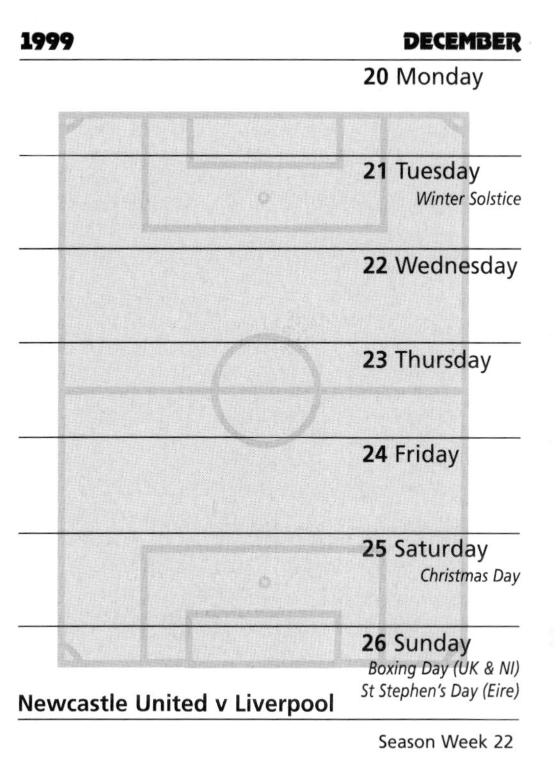

20 Monday

21 Tuesday
Winter Solstice

22 Wednesday

23 Thursday

24 Friday

25 Saturday
Christmas Day

26 Sunday
Boxing Day (UK & NI)
St Stephen's Day (Eire)

Newcastle United v Liverpool

This Time Last Year...

A brief FA Cup run that started with an emphatic win at Vale Park – goals courtesy of Owen, Ince and Fowler – and ended narrowly in the last minutes at Old Trafford later in the month left the Reds to concentrate on the Premiership. And that went pretty well, with a goalless draw at Highbury and a 7-1 thrashing of Southampton that included Robbie Fowler's second hat-trick of the campaign. Also on the scoresheet was youngster David Thompson, registering his first goal of the season and second for the club. He would make 14 appearances in total during 1998-99, ten of which were as substitute.

Thrills To Come...

The first visit to Vicarage Road, Watford, for a decade will be a highlight for travelling Reds this January, along with an earlier trip south to White Hart Lane and a visit from Bryan Robson's Middlesbrough. Add the Fourth and Fifth Rounds of the FA Cup and it could be a good way to kick off the millennium!

This Month Last Season

Date	Comp	Venue	Opposition	Result
3	FAC	A	Port Vale	3-0
9	PL	A	Arsenal	0-0
16	PL	H	Southampton	7-1
24	FAC	A	Manchester Utd	1-2
30	PL	A	Coventry C	1-2

Michael Owen ▶

27 Monday
Bank Holiday

28 Tuesday
Bank Holiday

Liverpool v Wimbledon

29 Wednesday

30 Thursday

31 Friday
Bank Holiday

1 Saturday
New Year's Day

2 Sunday

3 Monday
Bank Holiday

Tottenham H v Liverpool

4 Tuesday
Bank Holiday (Scotland only)

5 Wednesday

6 Thursday

7 Friday

8 Saturday

FA Cup Fourth Round

9 Sunday

Record FA Cup win: 8-0 v Swansea (1990).

10 Monday

11 Tuesday

12 Wednesday

Worthington Cup Semi-Final 1

13 Thursday

14 Friday

15 Saturday

Watford v Liverpool

16 Sunday

17 Monday

18 Tuesday

Peter Beardsley born in Newcastle (1961).

19 Wednesday

Steve Staunton born in Drogheda, Eire (1969).

20 Thursday

21 Friday

22 Saturday

Liverpool v Middlesbrough

23 Sunday

Bob Paisley born near Durham (1919).

This Time Last Year...

One win, two defeats and a draw made the short month of February 1999 a less than a sweet one for Liverpool. Song and Ferri – no relation to Bryan, we assume – were new names on the team sheet as Gérard Houllier shuffled his pack to find his best team. The Steve McManaman 'is he isn't he' saga wasn't helping, either...but on the plus side Michael Owen was returning to the scoresheet after a relatively fallow period. He netted three times in the four February games.

Thrills To Come...

Leeds, Arsenal and Leicester present an interesting challenge this time round, the first two at least likely fellow title contenders. The Worthington Cup Final could give the Reds their first piece of silverware in five years – don't forget they monopolised the trophy as the Milk Cup with four consecutive wins in the early 1980s. Add the FA Cup Sixth Round and Gérard's boys could well have the scent of success in their nostrils.

This Month Last Season

Date	Comp	Venue	Opposition	Result
6	PL	H	Middlesbrough	3-1
13	PL	A	Charlton Ath	0-1
20	PL	H	West Ham Utd	2-2
27	PL	A	Chelsea	1-2

Paul Ince ▶

Carlsberg

24 Monday

25 Tuesday

26 Wednesday

Worthington Cup Semi-Final 2

27 Thursday

28 Friday

Jamie Carragher born in Bootle (1978).

29 Saturday

FA Cup Fifth Round

30 Sunday

31 Monday

1 Tuesday

Record attendance of 61,905 at FA Cup Fourth Round clash against Wolves (1952).

2 Wednesday

3 Thursday

4 Friday

5 Saturday

Liverpool v Leeds United

Gareth Roberts born in Wrexham (1978).

6 Sunday

7 Monday

8 Tuesday

Stephen Wright born in Liverpool (1980).

9 Wednesday

10 Thursday

11 Friday

12 Saturday

Arsenal v Liverpool

13 Sunday

Former manager Bob Paisley dies (1996).

14 Monday

15 Tuesday

16 Wednesday

17 Thursday

Record League victory: 10-1 v Rotherham Town (1896).

18 Friday

19 Saturday

FA Cup Sixth Round

20 Sunday

MARCH ACTION

This Time Last Year...

With Cup action going on elsewhere and Liverpool not involved, March 1999 was a tale of just one game – an entertaining but disappointing defeat at Pride Park, Derby by three goals to two. The Reds didn't get off to the best of starts, allowing Deon Burton a free header at an 11th-minute corner, but a surging run from Michael Owen brought a penalty which was converted by strike partner Robbie Fowler. Derby, however, reclaimed the lead just before the interval when Paulo Wanchope headed past David James. Another goal for the Costa Rican four minutes after the restart left Liverpool with everything to do and, although Fowler claimed his second after a good run from Dominic Matteo shortly before the hour-mark, it was the Rams who ended the day three points to the good.

Thrills To Come...

Again, it comes down to a single fixture – purely in a manner of speaking . The 4 March visit to Old Trafford makes March 2000 a mighty month by anyone's reckoning, and after this clash of the giants anything else may well be a bit of an anti-climax. Visits from Sunderland and Newcastle sandwich yet another trip to Pride Park, when the Reds will be hoping for better luck this time round.

This Month Last Season

Date	Comp	Venue	Opposition	Result
13	PL	A	Derby County	2-3

Robbie Fowler ▶

Carlsberg
REDKNAPP
11

21 Monday

22 Tuesday

Kenny Dalglish resigns as manager (1991).

23 Wednesday

Ash Wednesday

24 Thursday

25 Friday

26 Saturday

Liverpool v Leicester C

27 Sunday

Worthington Cup Final

28 Monday

29 Tuesday

1 Wednesday
St David's Day

2 Thursday

3 Friday

4 Saturday

Kenny Dalglish born in Glasgow (1951).

Man United v Liverpool

5 Sunday

6 Monday

7 Tuesday

8 Wednesday

9 Thursday

10 Friday

11 Saturday

Liverpool v Sunderland

12 Sunday

13 Monday

14 Tuesday

15 Wednesday

16 Thursday

17 Friday
St Patrick's Day (NI & Eire)

Danny Murphy born in Chester (1977).

Derby Co v Liverpool

18 Saturday

19 Sunday
Mothering Sunday

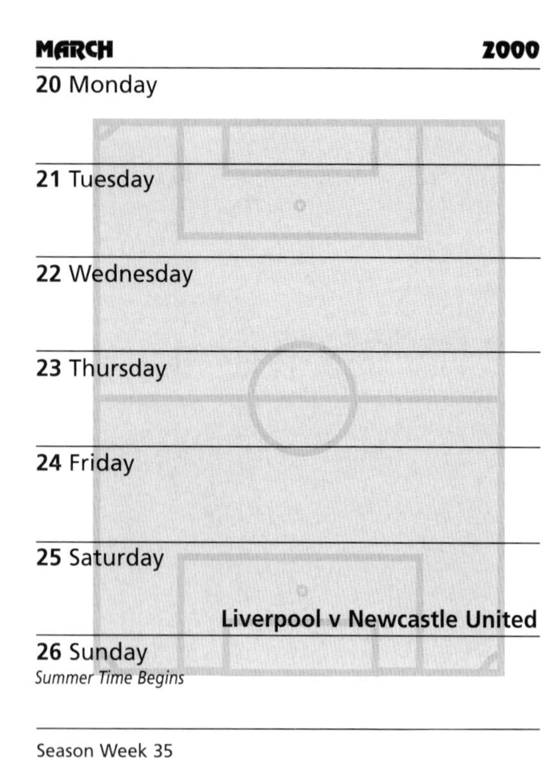

20 Monday

21 Tuesday

22 Wednesday

23 Thursday

24 Friday

25 Saturday

Liverpool v Newcastle United

26 Sunday

Summer Time Begins

27 Monday

Liverpool win their fourth consecutive League Cup (1984).

28 Tuesday

29 Wednesday

30 Thursday

31 Friday

1 Saturday
All Fools' Day

Coventry C v Liverpool

2 Sunday

APRIL ACTION

This Time Last Year...

The derby with Everton will be remembered not for the 3-2 scoreline but Robbie Fowler's antics after his goal. Shame for Patrik Berger, whose 82nd-minute strike proved to be the winner and topped off a great season for a player many thought would leave Anfield. Elsewhere, a win against Jason McAteer's Blackburn pushed them further towards the relegation trapdoor, while Michael Owen's season ended with a hamstring pull at Elland Road. He'd scored 17 goals in 30 League appearances, including one as sub, plus five more strikes in Cup competitions.

Thrills To Come...

Hopefully 9 April, the FA Cup Semi-Final date, will be one with meaning for the Reds this year. Otherwise there's six fixtures, including a trip across Stanley Park to Goodison. The last three visits brought two draws and a defeat so it's high time that Liverpool came away with something to shout about.

This Month Last Season

Date	Comp	Venue	Opposition	Result
3	PL	H	Everton	3-2
5	PL	A	Nott'm Forest	2-2
12	PL	A	Leeds Utd	0-0
17	PL	H	Aston Villa	0-1
21	PL	H	Leicester C	0-1
24	PL	A	Blackburn R	3-1

Patrik Berger ▶

Carlsberg

3 Monday

4 Tuesday

5 Wednesday

6 Thursday

7 Friday

8 Saturday

Liverpool v Tottenham H

9 Sunday

Robbie Fowler born in Liverpool (1975).

FA Cup Semi-Final

Ian Callaghan born in Liverpool (1942).

10 Monday

11 Tuesday

12 Wednesday

13 Thursday

14 Friday

Tragedy strikes in the FA Cup Semi-Final at Hillsborough (1985).

Wimbledon v Liverpool

15 Saturday

16 Sunday
Palm Sunday

17 Monday

18 Tuesday

19 Wednesday

20 Thursday

21 Friday

Good Friday Bank Holiday

22 Saturday

Everton v Liverpool

23 Sunday

St George's Day

Dominic Matteo born in Dumfries (1974).

24 Monday
Easter Monday Bank Holiday

Liverpool v Aston Villa

25 Tuesday

26 Wednesday

27 Thursday

28 Friday

Liverpool win the first of their record 18 League titles (1901).

29 Saturday

Chelsea v Liverpool

30 Sunday

1 Monday
May Day Holiday

2 Tuesday

3 Wednesday

4 Thursday

5 Friday

6 Saturday

Jorgen Nielsen born in Nykabing, Denmark (1971).

Liverpool v Southampton

7 Sunday

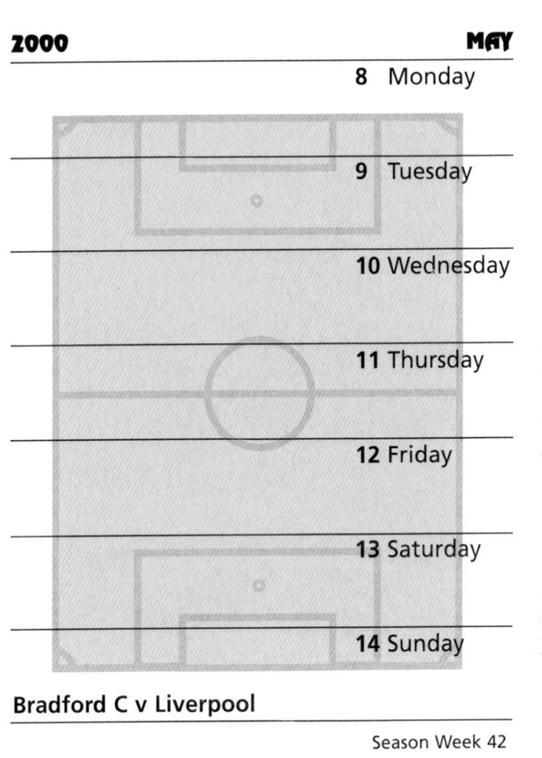

8 Monday

9 Tuesday

10 Wednesday

11 Thursday

12 Friday

13 Saturday

14 Sunday

Bradford C v Liverpool

This Time Last Year...

Two wins in four matches ended a season that had promised much but achieved relatively little. That said, who'd trade Paul Ince's 88th-minute equaliser at Anfield against Champions-elect Man United, wiping the smile off certain smug faces? Spurs cheekily came to Merseyside and built up a two-goal lead, but Redknapp, Ince and the soon to depart Steve McManaman pulled things back in front of a creditable 44,000 crowd. A visit to Hillsborough, never the happiest of hunting grounds given past events, saw the Reds slip to a single-goal defeat, but three goals against Wimbledon in the final match served notice that Liverpool intended to be back among the honours in 2000.

Thrills To Come...

After a visit from Southampton (here's hoping for another 7-1 scoreline!), the first season of the new millennium ends at Valley Parade, a ground the Reds haven't seen much of in years past. On the other hand, the following Saturday is reserved for the FA Cup Final – could this be a Red letter day at last?

This Month Last Season

Date	Comp	Venue	Opposition	Result
1	PL	H	Tottenham H	3-2
5	PL	H	Manchester Utd	2-2
8	PL	A	Sheffield Wed	0-1
16	PL	H	Wimbledon	3-0

Steve McManaman ▶

COM

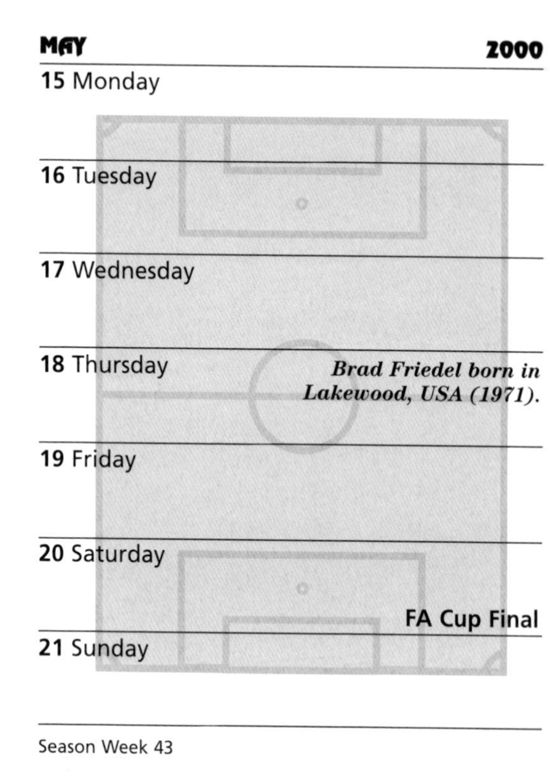

15 Monday

16 Tuesday

17 Wednesday

18 Thursday

Brad Friedel born in Lakewood, USA (1971).

19 Friday

20 Saturday

FA Cup Final

21 Sunday

22 Monday

23 Tuesday

24 Wednesday

Liverpool win the European Cup (1977).

25 Thursday

26 Friday

27 Saturday

28 Sunday

29 Monday
Spring Bank Holiday (UK & NI)

30 Tuesday

Steve Gerrard born in Whiston (1980).

31 Wednesday

1 Thursday

2 Friday

3 Saturday

4 Sunday

5 Monday
June Holiday (Eire only)

6 Tuesday

7 Wednesday

8 Thursday

9 Friday

10 Saturday

11 Sunday

QUESTION TIME

1. Which keeper was signed from Vitesse Arnhem in June 1999 for a British record £4 million?
2. Who is Liverpool's assistant manager?
3. How many times have Liverpool won the League Championship?
4. Which Swiss star was signed from Blackburn in the close season?
5. Who was the only player to start every UEFA Cup match during the 1998-99 campaign?
6. Which player signed from Crewe went back there on loan?
7. Name the last trophy Liverpool won prior to the start of the 1999-2000 season...
8. Who played the first two months of last season in goal?
9. Which former Anfield keeper was on Southampton's books last season?
10. Which two players made the most League appearances in 1998-99?
11. What country does Rigobert Song hail from?
12. Who scored the first goal of Liverpool's 1998-99 Premiership season?
13. Which two sides did Liverpool fail to score against last season?
14. To which Spain-bound international did Liverpool say goodbye in 1999?
15. Who holds the record for most appearances in a Red shirt?

(More questions opposite)

QUESTION TIME

(Continued)

16. Which two Liverpool legends are now at the Celtic helm?
17. Who left Anfield for his third Lancashire club in early 1999?
18. Which team was hit for seven at Anfield?
19. Who had a nasty collision with a post?
20. How many hat-tricks did Michael Owen notch last season?
21. Which club did long-serving Rob Jones sign for in summer 1999?
22. Which South African made only three sub appearances in the 1998-99 League campaign?
23. Who are Liverpool's sponsors?
24. Which former Liverpool player brought his Second Division team back to Anfield in the Worthington Cup?
25. Name the keeper loaned to Celtic in late 1998.
26. What nationality is new centre-back Sami Hyypia?
27. Who takes Liverpool's penalties?
28. Which Liverpool favourite returned to Anfield after an absence of seven years?
29. To which team was David James transferred in summer 1999?
30. How many European Cups have Liverpool won?

(Answers on last page)

12 Monday

13 Tuesday

14 Wednesday

15 Thursday

16 Friday

17 Saturday

Bjorn Kvarme born in Trondheim, Norway (1972).

18 Sunday

Father's Day

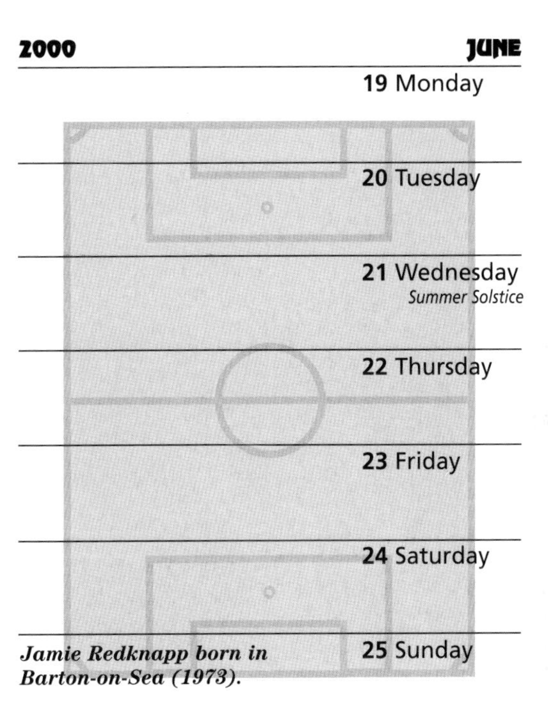

19 Monday

20 Tuesday

21 Wednesday

Summer Solstice

22 Thursday

23 Friday

24 Saturday

25 Sunday

Jamie Redknapp born in Barton-on-Sea (1973).

26 Monday

27 Tuesday

28 Wednesday

29 Thursday

30 Friday

1 Saturday

Rigobert Song born in Cameroon (1976).

2 Sunday

3 Monday

4 Tuesday

5 Wednesday

6 Thursday

7 Friday

8 Saturday

9 Sunday

10 Monday

11 Tuesday

12 Wednesday
Battle of the Boyne (NI)

Bill Shankly signs Ray Kennedy, then announces his retirement (1974).

13 Thursday

Vegard Heggem born in Norway (1975).

14 Friday

15 Saturday

16 Sunday

Gérard Houllier appointed joint manager (1998).

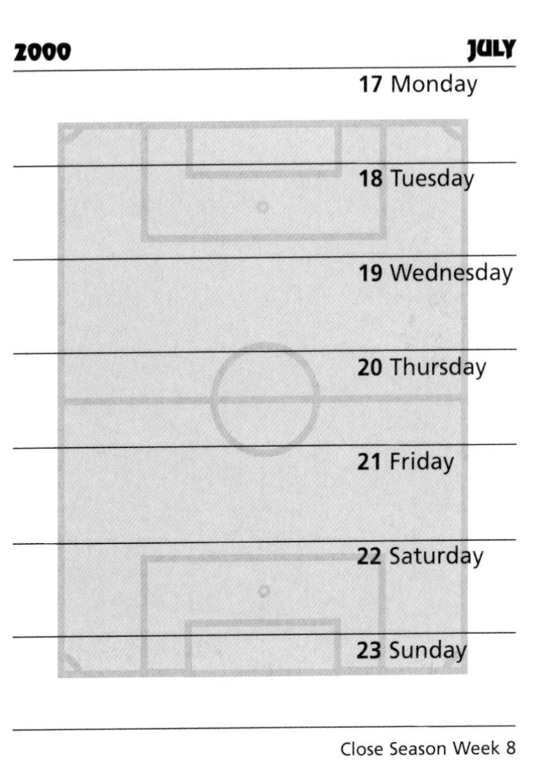

17 Monday

18 Tuesday

19 Wednesday

20 Thursday

21 Friday

22 Saturday

23 Sunday

24 Monday

25 Tuesday

26 Wednesday

27 Thursday

28 Friday

29 Saturday

30 Sunday

Anfield favourite Roger Hunt helps England win the World Cup at Wembley (1966).